THE LOST LAMB

WRITTEN BY

MELODY CARLSON

ILLUSTRATED BY

STEVE BJÖRKMAN

CANDLE
BOOKS

Published in the UK by Candle Books 2003.

Distributed by STL, P.O. Box 300, Carlisle CA3 0QS

Design by Cindy Kiple

ISBN 1 85985 485 0

Worldwide co-edition organized and produced by

Angus Hudson Ltd, Concorde House, Grenville Place, Mill Hill, London NW7 3SA, England.

Tel: +44 20 8959 3668   Fax: +44 20 8959 3678   coed@angushudson.com

Printed in Singapore

MELODY CARLSON *was a teacher and senior editor before becoming a best-selling author. She has written twenty books.*

STEVE BJÖRKMAN has illustrated several children's books. His whimsical artwork also appears widely in magazines and on greeting cards.

I can see the setting sun,

Telling me the day is done.

It's time to put my flock to bed.

My little lambs have sleepy heads.

Around the lake, beneath the ridge,

Across the meadow, over the bridge,

Down the hill, through the valley,

No time left to dilly-dally.

I see the farm – it is near.

At last, at last, we're finally here!

Come on, sheep – now don't be late,

I'll count your noses at the gate.

A hundred sheep are quite a few.

I know them all – from lamb to ewe.

And each one means a lot to me,

I call their names from A to Z.

There's Alex, Anna, Begonia, and Belle,

Clarence and Casey, Dexter and Del,

There's Edgar and Eva, Felix and Floss,

Gracie and Gertrude and Hairy and Hoss.

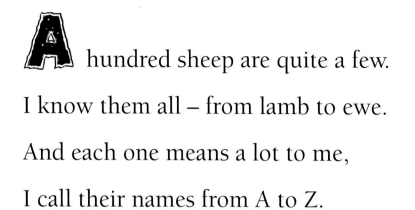

lack sheep, white sheep, spotted sheep, plain,

I count them all – each one by name.

Sly sheep, shy sheep, grumpy sheep too.

Why, I could start my own sheep zoo!

I count and count – it's almost night.

But that's okay, I'll get it right.

Molly, Nettie, Ollie, and Pom,

Quentin, Rowdy, Sugar, and Tom.

I'm almost finished. Just a few more sheep.

Then off to bed to get some sleep.

Walt's ninety-seven…Xavier's ninety-eight . . .

Yolanda Ewe is ninety-nine – but wait a minute!

WAIT!

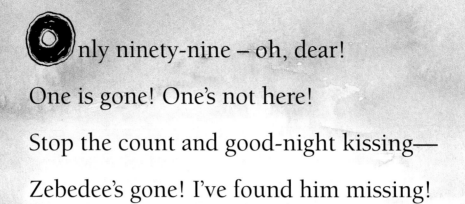

Only ninety-nine – oh, dear!

One is gone! One's not here!

Stop the count and good-night kissing—

Zebedee's gone! I've found him missing!

The rest of you may take a snooze,

But I must go – no time to lose!

Sweet dreams to you, my other sheep.

With one lost lamb, I cannot sleep.

By the light of soft moon-glow,

Into the night, I quickly go.

I cannot doze, I cannot sleep

Until I find my one lost sheep.

I've no time to dilly-dally.

I climb the hill, beyond the valley.

I cross the meadow, after the bridge,

I see the lake, just past the ridge.

And everywhere I go, I shout,

"Where are you, Zebedee? Come out!

I'm here to take you home with me.

Where have you gone, dear Zebedee?"

Beyond the ridge, caught on a thorn,

I spy my lamb – his fleece is torn!

I hear him crying out to me.

At last, I've found my Zebedee!

Oh, Zebedee, dear little lamb,

Do you know how glad I am,

To find you in the dark of night?

You gave my heart a fearful fright!

Now I can see you've had a scare,

But you can trust your shepherd's care,

So never wander far from me.

I'll keep you safe, my Zebedee.

Now I can see the rising sun.

The day is here, the night is done.

Of course, I'm tired, it is true,

But I'm so glad that I found you.

Wake up, you sheep, it's getting late!

Now, it's time to celebrate!

Look who's here – safe and sound.

My lamb was lost, but now he's found!

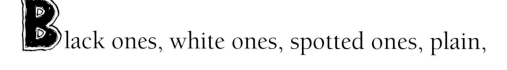

Black ones, white ones, spotted ones, plain,

I know my sheep – each one by name.

I love them all quite equally,

From Abigail to Zebedee.

If one gets lost, I leave the rest;

I search all night, I give my best.

I find the lamb who's lost to me,

And bring him home so joyfully!

. . . If a man has a hundred sheep,

and one of them goes astray,

does he not leave the ninety-nine

and go to the mountains

and seek the one who is straying?

And if he should find it,

assuredly, I say to you,

he rejoices more over that sheep

than the ninety-nine

that did not go astray.

MATTHEW 18:12-13 (NKJV)